The Ultimate
Rib-Tickling, Beer-Swilling
Ice-and-a-Slice Quiz

Series Editor: Colleen Collier
Research: Jane Purcell
Contributor: Sue Curran
Page Layout and Design: Louise Millar
Cover Design: Gary Inwood Studios

Published by:
LAGOON BOOKS
PO BOX 311, KT2 5QW, UK
PO BOX 990676, Boston, MA 02199, USA

www.lagoongames.com

ISBN: 1-902813-45-6

Printed in Singapore

The Ultimate
Rib-Tickling, Beer-Swilling
Ice-and-a-Slice Quiz

LAGOON
BOOKS

INTRODUCTION

This book contains some of the wildest, wackiest and downright ridiculous trivia relating to drinking and booze ever assembled in one place. It quite simply makes for an excellent read, but if you're the competitive sort you can always…

HOST YOUR OWN DRINKING TRIVIA QUIZ!

The questions have all been divided into categories, and there are five in total…

 History

 Art and Literature

 Film and Television

 Music

 General Knowledge

The numbers on the page edge (2, 4, 6, 8, & 10) refer to the point value that is scored for a correct answer. You will also notice that on certain quizzes, there is a bonus star above one of the questions. On the opposite page, a corresponding question and point value can be found.

Players form two or more teams and a question master is appointed. Teams then take it in turns to choose a category, and the question master reads out the appropriate category question (the answers start on p66). Each correct answer scores the point value next to the chosen question. If a team answers incorrectly, the first team to 'buzz' in and answer correctly will be awarded half the points originally on offer. (Each team should be allotted a 'buzzer' sound – the sillier, the better!).

If a team picks one of the questions that has the bonus star above it, and answers that question correctly, they then are given the bonus question to answer (found on the opposite page). If they answer correctly again, they are awarded the allotted points as a bonus. If, however, they answer the bonus question incorrectly, they do not receive the points and the other team/s can 'buzz' in and win the points on offer.

The question master keeps score, and has the final decision in any disputes. The team with the highest score at the end wins.

Have fun!

QUIZ 1

The walls of 'The Magdala' pub in Hampstead, England, still show the bullet holes from a murder committed by…
a) Jack the Ripper b) Ruth Ellis c) Al Capone

10

Where does 'Let us eat and drink for tomorrow we die', come from?
a) 'Henry V' by Shakespeare
b) 'The Old Man and the Sea' by Hemingway
c) The Book of Isaiah in the Old Testament

6

According to Dean Martin, you're not drunk if you can…
a) Remember who you are
b) Lie on the floor without holding on
c) Tie your tie, button your fly and remember which way is down

2

Which Eric Clapton song is about a bloated rock star, who is so drunk that his wife has to drive him home and undress him?

8

According to PJ O'Rourke, what is the only rule at the Commodore Bar in Beirut?

9

QUIZ 2

 Glen Turret, Scotland's oldest distillery dates from…
a) 1243
b) 1576
c) 1775

6

 Which American novelist observed, "First you take a drink, then the drink takes a drink, then the drink takes you"?

2

 Which actor played Tom Cruise's boss in the hit movie 'Cocktail'?

10

 Which legendary musician was arrested in Florida in 1969 and charged with profanity, drunkenness, and exposing himself onstage during a concert?

4

 What happens to an ant if it gets drunk?
a) It explodes
b) It falls over onto its right side
c) It walks backwards and makes a slight hissing sound

8

QUIZ 3

 In America, in 1790, an 'Anti-Fogmatic' was an alcoholic drink supposed to counteract the bad effects of fog. True or False?

4

 How did Krook, the gin-drinking rag-and-bone man in Charles Dickens' 'Bleak House' meet his bizarre end?

10

 Which John Wayne film has a famous fight scene, which breaks for drinks before resuming?
a) 'The Searchers'
b) 'The Quiet Man'
c) 'The Conqueror'

2

 Keith Moon was as famed for his hell-raising as he was for his musical talent. Which group did he play for?

8

 Which of these phrases describe extreme drunkenness in Australia?
a) As pissed as a possum
b) As wrecked as a 'roo
c) As drunk as Chloe

6

QUIZ 4

English MP William Pitt (the Younger) was prescribed a bottle of port a day to cure his gout. How did he die?
a) Drunkenly falling in front of a carriage
b) From the pain of his gout
c) Cirrhosis of the liver

8

Which seventeenth-century English poet claimed to have stayed drunk for five years?
a) Jonathan Swift
b) The Second Earl of Rochester, John Wilmot
c) Lord Byron

2

Which actor plays Mickey Rourke and Matt Dillon's drunken father in the film 'Rumblefish'?

4

Which American singer/songwriter has written songs such as 'Jockey Full of Bourbon', 'Gin Soaked Boy' and 'The Piano Has Been Drinking, Not Me', and has played barmen in two Francis Ford Coppola films?

6

In sign language, whiskey is indicated by two fingers poked down the throat. True or False?

10

Which of the following is
not a real wine?
a) Grk
b) Lump
c) El Lager

QUIZ 5

Dionysus is the Roman god of fertility and wine. True or False?

6

From which novel does the following phrase come from – 'Those were drinking days and most men drink hard'?
a) 'The Sun Also Rises' by Ernest Hemingway
b) 'The Big Sleep' by Raymond Chandler
c) 'A Tale of Two Cities' by Charles Dickens

10

Who plays the bartender on the USS Enterprise in 'Star Trek: The Next Generation'?

BONUS

8

Which drink is mentioned in all the following songs – 'Death of a Clown' (by 'The Kinks'), 'Honky Tonk Woman' (by 'The Rolling Stones'), and 'Substitute' (by 'The Who')?

4

The expression 'The Real McCoy' comes from…
a) A Caribbean rumrunner
b) An Irish whiskey advertizing campaign from the 1890s
c) A special brew of Milwaukee 'heavy'

2

QUIZ 6

During World War I, Lloyd George said, "Drink is doing us more damage than all the _____ put together". Was it...
a) Powdered eggs
b) German submarines
c) Americans

4

Which thriller writer came up with the slogan 'Guinness is good for you' whilst working in advertizing?

2

What was the name of the creepy rural pub in the classic horror film, 'An American Werewolf in London'?

8

Which German composer spent his early career as a court musician, having to support his entire family because of his father's alcoholism?

10

Oscar Levant said, "I don't drink liquor. It...
a) ...makes me feel good"
b) ...makes me act like my father and think like my mother"
c) ...makes the sidewalk smaller"

6

QUIZ 7

 What happened for the last time in England on 11 June 1872 to drunkard Mark Tuck, as a result of him being an "incorrigible bacchanalian"? **10**

 Ben Johnson described claret as so weak, "that a man would be drowned by it before it made him drunk". True or False? **8**

 What drink does James Bond like "Shaken, not stirred"? **2**

 On the tercentenary of Mozart's death, a special sake was produced in Japan. To make it special…
a) The vat contained wood from Mozart's clavichord
b) Two of Mozart's descendants helped
c) Music by Mozart was played to assist fermentation **6**

 What is a 'dew drink'?
a) A drink before breakfast
b) A drink made with rainwater
c) A weak drink **4**

In 1959, Ermal Cleon Fraze invented something for which drinkers everywhere will be eternally grateful. What was it?
a) The bendy straw
b) Alka-Seltzer
c) The ring-pull

QUIZ 8

What is the origin of 'chunder', meaning 'to vomit'?

4

How did Dylan Thomas define an alcoholic?
a) Someone you don't like who drinks as much as you
b) Someone who sees nothing but horror in an empty bottle
c) Someone with a mortal fear of hangovers

2

What was the name of the invisible six-foot rabbit that accompanied James Stewart's alcoholic millionaire character everywhere in the film of the same name?

8

Who said "I'd hate to be a teetotaler. Imagine getting up in the morning and knowing that's as good as you're going to feel all day"?
a) Dean Martin
b) Keith Richards
c) Elvis Presley

10

From which country does the word 'grog' come from?

BONUS

6

QUIZ 9

According to legend, which ancient civilization was taught to brew beer by a god?
a) Greeks
b) Romans
c) Egyptians

2

Name the Eugene O'Neill play that is set in Harry Hope's bar and features a group of whiskey-ridden derelicts.

6

In 'The Hitchhiker's Guide to the Galaxy', what is the name of the dangerously strong drink favored by Zaphod Beeblebrox and Ford Prefect?

8

Which US city was 'The Blues Brothers' set in?

4

What is a 'sconce'?
a) An Oxford University beer challenge
b) A small semi-private room in an English pub
c) A loud boorish drunk

10

QUIZ 10

In 1970, a drunken Japanese motorist drove over a mile without…
a) Realizing he was in reverse
b) His recently severed arm
c) Realizing he had mistakenly climbed into a light aircraft

8

Which drink is mentioned several times in Hemingway's novel, 'For Whom the Bell Tolls' because of its erotic powers?

2

David Niven and Errol Flynn's Hollywood home was nicknamed 'Cirrhosis by the Sea'. True or False?

10

Who recorded the original version of the popular song 'Red Red Wine'?

6

What is a 'pundy'?
a) A beer belly
b) A free ration of beer for brewers
c) Enough beer to make you very drunk

4

What is a 'Dog's Nose'?
a) A cocktail of beer and gin
b) A traditional English name for a
   hop-masher's pummel
c) A weeping sore on the lips caused
   by drinking from dirty glasses

QUIZ 11

 In the grounds of Winchester Cathedral, a man is buried who died from…
a) Drinking too much 'small beer' on a hot day
b) Drinking cider after a 'surfeit of young turnip'
c) Singing hymns heartily after consuming 'an ill-fitting measure' of communion wine

10

 In 1986, according to the 'Encyclopedia Americana', two million Americans could be classified as alcoholics. True or False?

 BONUS **2**

 Richard Burton played a brooding alcoholic in the film 'Come Back, Little Sheba'. True or False?

4

 Name the three main hard-drinking members of 'The Rat Pack'.

6

 In Australia, what drink is 'Squatter's Daughter' slang for?
a) Weak beer
b) Water
c) A very small drink (a quarter)

8

QUIZ 12

Why did Ancient Greek drinkers wear wreaths?
a) To show their relative drinking prowess
b) As a mark of respect to the vine and Bacchus
c) To protect themselves from the drink's
   noxious fumes

6

Why did novelist Graham Greene never drink
liqueurs?

2

In the film 'Animal House', what is the name of
John Belushi's character who downs a bottle
of bourbon in one draught?

4

Which great jazz musician died prematurely
at the age of 34 from cirrhosis of the liver, and
whose life story movie was made by Clint
Eastwood?

8

What is a 'God-forbid-me'?
a) A very strong beer, brewed one day a year
   by Franciscan friars
b) A mixture of rum, gin and sour milk, used
   as a morning-after 'never again' cure
c) An enormous two-handled drinking mug

10

QUIZ 13

In seventeenth-century hospitals, children were given two gallons of beer a week. True or False?

2

Which writer does Mickey Rourke play in the film 'Barfly'?

10

Which actress played an alcoholic in the film 'When a Man Loves a Woman'?
a) Meg Ryan
b) Demi Moore
c) Darryl Hannah

4

Complete the name of the Motorhead single, '_____ and Alcohol'.
a) Pills
b) Milk
c) Drugs

8

What is 'Poteen'?

6

What happens to goldfish immersed in 3.1 per cent alcohol?

a) They overturn in six to eight minutes
b) They lose the use of their right fin, thus swimming in tight circles
c) Their swim bladders rupture and their gills dilate, causing them to drown

QUIZ 14

Which vegetable would the Egyptians rest on their foreheads to cure a hangover?

8

Famous wit, Dorothy Parker, once said,
"One more drink and I'll be under…
a) …the table"
b) …the carpet"
c) …the host"

6

Complete the following piece of bar room BONUS
wisdom from Norm in 'Cheers', "Women, can't live with them…
a) …can't live without them"
b) …don't want to"
c) …pass the beer nuts"

10

Splodgenessabounds had chart success with a song entitled 'Two Pints of Lager and a Packet of Crisps, Please'. True or False?

4

In semaphore, an alcoholic drink is represented by whirling one flag circularly about the head, whilst patting the stomach with the other. True or False?

2

18

QUIZ 15

When did canned beer first appear in Britain?
a) 1935
b) 1955
c) 1962

4

Which playwright famously said, "Alcohol is the anesthesia by which we endure the operation of life"?

6

In the Peter Sellers Cold War comedy film 'Dr Strangelove', why will Col Ripper mix only rainwater with his bourbon?

2

'Brewer's Droop' had a surprise chart hit in the UK in 1974 with 'Somerset Cider Inside Her'. True or False?

10

Traditionally, Guinness is made with water from which river?
a) The Shannon
b) The Moine
c) The Liffey

8

QUIZ 16

In 1998, which US town had the highest rate of alcoholism?
a) Miami, Florida
b) Reno, Nevada
c) Provo, Utah

4

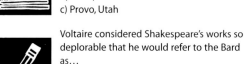

Voltaire considered Shakespeare's works so deplorable that he would refer to the Bard as…
a) "That talentless scribe"
b) "That drunken fool"
c) "That overrated drunken scribbler"

10

Which riotous sorority house film contains the immortal line, "Fat, drunk and stupid is no way to go through life, son"?

2

Late actor, Oliver Reed, once made an appearance on television and belted out a classic song from 'The Trogs'. What was its title?

8

Which organization was responsible for making beer in metal kegs popular in the UK?
a) The British Government
b) The Tax Office
c) The US Air Force

6

In 1668, Dom Perignon (a blind cellarmaster)
discovered Champagne and said…
a) "Oh, come quickly. I am drinking the stars"
b) "The bubbles have gone straight up my nose"
c) "I'm going to make a fortune"

QUIZ 17

In 1814, a huge storage vat of porter (a bitter beer brewed from charred or browned malt) exploded in Liquorpond Street, London, destroying three houses and killing eight people. True or False?

BONUS

8

Which member of the Brontë family developed a fondness for drink and opium?

4

Which film about a drinker won Best Actor and Best Picture Oscars in 1946?

6

Which of the following singers did not die from a drink or drugs overdose?
a) Marc Bolan
b) Jimi Hendrix
c) Janis Joplin

10

What is a 'scuppernong'?
a) A Maori name for an alcoholic drink
b) A type of white grape
c) An Anglo-Saxon drinking helmet

2

QUIZ 18

In the court of Henry VIII, a page who made a handmaiden pregnant had his beer ration stopped for a month. True or False?

10

Who said, "Always do sober what you said you'd do drunk. That will teach you to keep your mouth shut"?
a) F Scott Fitzgerald
b) Ernest Hemingway
c) Lord Byron

6

In the film 'Mash', what was Radar's favorite drink?

2

In the musical 'Cabaret', what is Sally Bowles' favorite hangover cure?

8

Complete this old English proverb, 'Good ale will make a cat...
a) ...speak'
b) ...bark'
c) ...bad ale will make a rat'

4

QUIZ 19

The Manhattan cocktail was invented by…
a) Winston Churchill's mother
b) F Scott Fitzgerald's father
c) Frank Sinatra's grandmother

4

Whose dying words were, "Drink to me"?
a) Pablo Picasso
b) Dylan Thomas
c) Dorothy Parker

10

David Niven said of which friend and chronic drinker, "You could always rely on him to let you down"?

2

Which classical composer died of cholera in 1893 after drinking unboiled water?

6

Which popular drink has an English name derived from the Hebrew word 'Shekar'?

8

What was considered a must at fashionable
seventeenth-century social events?
a) Drinking champagne out of unmarried ladies'
   dance slippers
b) Drinking chocolate mixed with milk, wine,
   or beer
c) Drinking cider laced with Calvados

QUIZ 20

Where does the word 'Pils' come from?

2

'The Sorrows of Gin' was adapted by which American playwright?
a) Wendy Wasserstein
b) Clifford Odets
c) Tennessee Williams

10

Who replaced River Phoenix in the hit movie, 'Interview with a Vampire' after his drink and drugs related death?
a) Leonardo di Caprio
b) Christian Slater
c) Toby McQuire

6

Which hard-drinking American singer was better known as 'The Empress of the Blues'?

8

What does VSOP stand for? BONUS

4

QUIZ 21

The Sumerian goddess of drinking was called 'Burpa'. True or False?

2

Which Biblical character had to be dressed by his son after flooding himself with wine?

4

Which brand of beer does Homer Simpson drink?

6

'The Wurzels' had a top ten hit with the song…
a) 'I am a Scrumpy Drinker'
b) 'I am a Cider Drinker'
c) 'Get Off My Land'

8

In Australia, if you 'drink with the flies', you…
a) Drink hardly anything
b) Drink alone
c) Drink anything you can get your hands on

10

QUIZ 22

In Medieval England, the lord's beer taster would check quality by...
a) Pouring a pint over his head
b) Making his dog drink half a gallon
c) Pouring a pint on a chair and then sitting in it wearing leather trousers

8

The first words of Shakespeare's play, 'The Taming of the Shrew' are uttered by which drunken character?
a) Christopher Sly b) Petruchio c) The Hostess

4

Which eighties 'Brat Pack' actor said to the officer when arrested for drunk driving, "Drunk definitely, but I don't know if you could call it driving"?

6

Which influential country music star died in 1953, at the age of 30, from alcohol and drug abuse?

10

In which country did alcohol-free lager originate?

2

What is the strongest proof any liquor can be?
a) 92 per cent
b) 99 per cent
c) 97 per cent

QUIZ 23

In the eighteenth century, the ordinary man's allowance of beer was a gallon each working day. True or False?

10

Which sixteenth-century writer said, "There are more old drunkards than old physicians"?
a) Francois Rabelais
b) Ludovico Ariosto
c) John Calvin

8

Which Japanese TV series popularized drinking red wine in Japan?
a) Shogun
b) Shitsurakuen
c) Kamikaze

6

BONUS

Which singer/songwriter's first solo album entitled 'Piano Man' was inspired by his six-month music stint in a Los Angeles bar?

4

Most beer is clarified with a substance extracted from…
a) Pig's kidneys
b) Sheep's pancreases
c) Fish's air bladders

2

QUIZ 24

When was lager first brewed in Britain?
a) 1301
b) 1879
c) 1929

6

In Shakespeare's 'Richard III', how does the Duke of Clarence die? He drowns in…
a) A butt of malmsey
b) A casket of ale
c) The sea

10

Which US city is 'Cheers' set in?

8

Which drunk and debauched Emperor allegedly sang arias while Rome burned?

4

In which European country does an autumnal beer-drinking extravaganza take place?

2

QUIZ 25

In the nineteenth century, swallowing ammonia was a popular hangover cure. True or False?

2

In 1593, the author of 'Dr Faustus' was killed in a drunken brawl at the 'Bull's Tavern' pub in Kent, England. Who was he?

4

Which film actress declared, "It's useless to hold a person to anything he says while he's in love, drunk or running for office"?
a) Marilyn Monroe
b) Shirley Maclaine
c) Elizabeth Taylor

6

The drummer John Bonham died from alcohol poisoning in 1980 and the rock group he played for subsequently split up. Who were they?

8

'Eck' is…
a) Sediment in a cask ale
b) A German vineyard
c) "Cheers" in Innuit

10

After California, which is the second largest
wine-producing state in the US?
a) Washington
b) Florida
c) New York

QUIZ 26

How did Sultan Sullivan I, punish drunkards?
a) He would have them ducked in a vat of
   sour wine
b) He tattooed the words, 'I am a Demon' on them
c) He poured molten lead down their throats

8

Which Roman philosopher and writer was
ordered to commit suicide by drinking a cup
of hemlock?
a) Socrates b) Sophocles c) Euripides

BONUS **10**

Actor River Phoenix died in 1993 from a
drug/alcohol overdose outside which
notorious Hollywood nightclub?

2

Which song by Barry Manilow was set in a
Cuban bar?

4

Who, when driven to drink by a beautiful
blonde woman, remarked, "It's the one thing
I'm indebted to her for"?

6

QUIZ 27

During the reign of 'Catherine the Great' of Russia, why were the Moscow ballrooms filled with women dressed as men?

6

Which children's book has the heroine growing to gigantic proportions after taking a swig from a bottle labeled 'Drink Me'?

2

What is the name of the barman at Homer Simpson's favorite drinking establishment?
a) Moe Syzlac
b) Montgomery Burns
c) Waylon Smithers

4

Who had a number one country hit with 'Two More Bottles of Wine' in 1978?

8

What was the name of the Hofmeister bear?
a) Ringo
b) George
c) Bramwell

10

QUIZ 28

Irish coffee was invented at Shannon airport on the west coast of Ireland.
True or False?

4

In Shakespeare's 'Henry IV, Part Two', Prince Hal parts company with his old drinking pal with the words, "I know thee not old man". To whom is he referring?
a) Bardolph b) Pistol c) Falstaff

6

Who was the hard-drinking director of the classic movie, 'The African Queen'?

10

The US national anthem, 'The Star Spangled Banner', was set to the tune of a drinking song. True or False?

2

Which country drinks most beer per head?
a) America
b) New Zealand
c) UK

8

In which state in Australia is it still constitutional law that all pubs have a railing outside for patrons to tie up their horse?
a) Queensland
b) New South Wales
c) Victoria

QUIZ 29

BONUS

In 1599, the commander of the English Navy entertained 6,000 guests with punch served by waiters floating in a punch bowl. True or False?

10

'Glass of Absinthe' was a cubist sculpture created by which twentieth-century artist?

8

Whose first line in movies was, "Gimme a Whiskey with ginger ale and don't be stingy baby"?
a) Greta Garbo
b) Marlene Dietrich
c) Lotte Lenya

6

'Long Neck Bottle' and 'Two Pina Coladas' are songs by which Country and Western star?

4

Which country produces the most wine?
a) Italy
b) France
c) USA

2

QUIZ 30

In old England, drunkards were forced to parade around in the 'Newcastle Jacket'. This was…
a) A lidless barrel with a head hole
b) A hessian sack filled with fish scraps
c) A wooden placard reading 'I am mine own damnation'

6

Which legendary American playwright confessed to alcoholism and drug addiction in 'Memoirs', published in 1979?

4

Which hell-raising actor died in a Maltese bar while on location filming the hit movie 'Gladiator'?

8

'Making your Mind Up', 'Land of Make Believe', and 'My Camera Never Lies', were hits for which UK pop group?
a) 'Bucks Fizz'
b) Iggy Pop
c) 'Champagne Charlies'

10

How many firkins are there in a butt?

8

QUIZ 31

In old England, what was a scuttlebutt?
a) A ship's water barrel
b) Someone who swept the tavern's floor in exchange for free drink
c) An enormous pewter beer jug, sufficient for a whole coach team

4

Which 'Romantic' poet was addicted to absinthe and, during a drunken quarrel, murdered his lover Verlaine?

10

Who plays the resident singer/pianist at the bar in the television series, 'Ally McBeal'?
a) Portia de Rossi
b) Calista Flockheart
c) Vonda Shepherd

8

Which rock band wrote the song 'My Wife', about a man trying to explain to his wife why he stayed out drinking three nights in a row?

2

Which US president was killed while his valet, his coachman and his bodyguard were boozing?

6

Who wrote the greatest song title of all time,
'I'd Rather Have a Bottle in Front of Me (Than
a Frontal Lobotomy)'?
a) Randy Hanzlick
b) Randy Socksniff
c) Randy Van Drijver

QUIZ 32

Which English monarch regularly breakfasted on a quart of ale?
a) Elizabeth I
b) Edward VII
c) William of Orange

2

Who wrote the classic novel, 'Cider with Rosie'?

6

Which child star of 'ET' was in rehab for drink and drugs while still in her teens?

10

In 1975, country diva Tammy Wynette filed for a real DIVORCE from her singing star husband. She alleged he had chased her round the house with a rifle during one of his frequent drunken rages. Who was he?

4

How does the organization 'Alcoholics Anonymous' define an alcoholic?
a) A person who drinks in order to get drunk
b) A person who drinks in secret
c) A person who cannot control their drinking

BONUS

8

QUIZ 33

Which of the following is early-American slang for liquor?
a) Tooth-rot
b) Cheek blush
c) Nose paint

6

Which 'Vogue' editor, on appointment to the magazine, banned all alcohol from the premises during working hours?

10

Which creepy film character ate the liver of one of his victims, accompanied by "Fava beans and a fine Chianti"?

2

Which singer/songwriter said of his alcoholism, "I never saw the tunnel. It's still hard to believe how close I ran to mortality"?

8

What does 'crapulent' mean?
a) Weak bladdered
b) Prone to sadness when drinking
c) Frequently indulging in alcohol

4

QUIZ 34

The word 'hooch' comes from the Hoochino people. Where do they come from?
a) Iceland
b) Alaska
c) Siberia

2

Who wrote 'The Cocktail Party'?

4

Which former hell-raising actor drank two bottles of Chateau Margaux before giving up alcohol for good?

6

In which Rossini opera does Count Almaviva disguise himself as a homeless drunken soldier in order to get into his beloved's house?

8

Which of the following is not a real French wine?
a) Le Pis
b) Les Migraines
c) Chateau Cilla

10

What is potophobia?
a) Fear of drinks
b) Fear of water
c) Fear of pubs

QUIZ 35

In 1735, the British annual gin consumption was…
a) 400,000 gallons
b) 1,700,000 gallons
c) 11,000,000 gallons

8

After years of heavy drinking, how did Ernest Hemingway die?

4

BONUS

Which rotund cinematic legend was the voice behind the Carlsberg lager commercials?

10

Name the alcoholic singer/actress who in 1964 appeared in concert with her daughter.

2

Arrack is an aniseed spirit, similar to ouzo. What does 'arrack' mean in Arabic?
a) The water that cleanses
b) Sweat
c) Mother's milk

6

46

QUIZ 36

'Pimpeltjens' is a word of Dutch origin. It is…
a) A pus-colored liqueur
b) The traditional Dutch barman's apron
c) The name of an alcoholic foreign secretary who disgraced himself on national TV

6

In 'A Streetcar Named Desire', what is the drink that Blanche du Bois often requests?

10

Who accepted the role of hard-drinking Quint in the movie 'Jaws', after it had been turned down by Lee Marvin?

2

'Everybody Loves Somebody' was a US number one in 1964 for whom?

8

'Ullage' is…
a) A single malt from the Outer Hebrides
b) The distance between the wine and the cork in a bottle
c) A dry white French wine similar to Medoc

4

QUIZ 37

What year did Guinness start brewing?
a) 1698
b) 1759
c) 1807

8

Which Sean O'Casey play features a woman whose drunken husband wrongly assumes he is to inherit a fortune and spends accordingly?

6

Which alcoholic footballer who had a film made about his life said, "I'm attending Alcoholics Anonymous, but it's difficult to remain anonymous"?
a) David Beckham
b) Norman Whiteside
c) George Best

4

Which Oasis album are the following lyrics taken from – "I was looking for some action, but all I found was cigarettes and alcohol"?

2

What is the name given to someone who collects beer-bottle labels?
a) A labologist
b) A pratologist
c) A labelarian

10

What year did beer start to be sold in bottles?
a) 1850
b) 1820
c) 1900

QUIZ 38

 'Bastard' was an eighteenth-century name for Claret. True or False?

4

 'The Bar at the *Folies Bergère*', a famous BONUS drinking establishment, was painted by which French Impressionist?

8

 In Quentin Tarantino's cult movie, 'Pulp Fiction', John Travolta takes Uma Thurman out to dinner. What does she drink?
a) A five-dollar milkshake
b) Neat bourbon
c) Champagne

6

 After one of the most successful British boy bands split up, who went on a drinking binge, then cleaned up his act and released a solo album entitled 'Life Thru a Lens'?

10

 WC Fields claimed he never drank "anything stronger than _____ before breakfast"?
a) Beer
b) Gin
c) Sherry

2

QUIZ 39

Who said, "Give my people plenty of beer, good beer and cheap beer, and you will have no revolution among them"?
a) Tzar Nicholas II
b) Fidel Castro
c) Queen Victoria

8

In which Anne Brontë novel does a Victorian heroine take the radical step of actually leaving her alcoholic husband and taking refuge under an assumed name?

4

Which Australian star of 'Crocodile Dundee' made a series of commercials for Fosters lager?

2

'Europe 72' is the last album by 'The Grateful Dead' to feature 'Pigpen', the hard-drinking keyboard player who died of liver failure in 1973. What was his real name?

10

In the UK in 1871, what proportion of the adult population was involved in the production and distribution of alcohol?
a) 0.04 per cent b) 2 per cent c) 8 per cent

6

QUIZ 40

In Medieval England, what was an 'ale-conner'?
a) The lord's professional ale tester
b) Someone who sold flavored barley water
c) A traveling master brewer

6

The famously inebriated British journalist, Jeffrey Bernard, inspired a play entitled 'Jeffrey Bernard is unwell'. Which notorious drinker played the leading role?

10

In the 1966 movie, 'Who's Afraid of Virginia Woolf', which real-life couple played the drunk and brawling Martha and George?

8

Which 1980s band wrote the lyrics, '…juices like wine and I'm hungry like the wolf'?

4

What is the highly toxic, fit-inducing ingredient of absinthe that caused it to be banned in most European countries?

2

Which of the following was a nineteenth-century cure for drunkenness?
a) Drinking a distilled liquid extracted from acorns
b) Drinking owls eggs which have been cracked into a cup
c) Placing a live eel in the drinker's full cup

QUIZ 41

 In which year did Prohibition in the US end?
a) 1933
b) 1934
c) 1935

2

 Which writer said, "All Irish whiskey uses the water of the Liffey, all but one filter it, but John Jameson's uses it, mud and all"?

8

 John Wayne finally received an Oscar in 1970 for playing a hard-drinking, but lovable, cowboy in which movie?

6

BONUS

 Which tragic rock star was portrayed by Bette Midler in 'The Rose'?

4

 On German beer, what does 'hell' refer to?
a) Its relative bite
b) Its color
c) Its brewing age

10

QUIZ 42

In 1911, famous escapologist Harry Houdini had to be rescued from a huge vat of Tetley's Beer. True or False?

6

Name the alcoholic French painter who spent weeks at a time in brothels painting the prostitutes (on canvas!).

4

Who played the shambolic, drunken English professor in 'Educating Rita'?
a) Michael Caine
b) Gary Oldman
c) Albert Finney

2

Who sang, 'I got the Sweetest Hangover'?

10

Which country's largest whiskey company is called 'Suntory'?
a) China
b) Japan
c) Korea

8

QUIZ 43

At one time, it was thought that carrying the ashes of the burnt livers of frogs and hedgehogs in a bag would cure alcohol-induced sexual impotence. True or False?

10

In 1877, Emile Zola wrote of the downfall of the Rougon-Macquart family through alcohol. What was the novel called?
a) 'L'Assomoir' b) 'Therese Racquin' c) 'Nana'

8

Which 1930s film star fell from grace after a starlet died at one of his parties?
a) Buster Keaton
b) Roscoe (Fatty) Arbuckle
c) Douglas Fairbanks Jr

4

Who wrote these song lyrics, 'Like a bird on a wire, like a drunk in a midnight choir, I have tried in my way to be free'?

6

What is Balderdash?

2

Who is the patron saint of beer and wine sellers?
a) St Guinevere of Calvados
b) St Marcus of Locksley
c) St Amand of Maastricht

QUIZ 44

The Etruscan god of wine was called…
a) Nurrlik
b) Fufluns
c) Nasti

4

The English poet, Elizabeth Barrett, spent years confined as an invalid. One popular Victorian 'medicine' she took was opium dissolved in alcohol. What was its more common name?

6

Name the two UK stars of the famous 'Cinzano' commercials

10

The father of which singer/songwriter was a bar-tending Seventh Day Adventist?
a) Little Richard
b) Chuck Berry
c) James Brown

2

Richter, Sykes and Cartier are methods of doing what?

BONUS

8

QUIZ 45

In Ireland, in 1978, what percentage of the price of whiskey was the cost of producing it?
a) 3 per cent
b) 23 per cent
c) 63 per cent

4

Who won an Obie (for Off-Broadway Theater) in 1968, for his role as the psychotic alcoholic in 'The Indian Wants the Bronx'?

6

Who played alcoholic actress Frances Farmer, in the movie of the same name?
a) Meryl Streep
b) Jessica Lange
c) Helen Hunt

8

The song 'Lilac Wine' was covered by which female folk singer?

2

Pernod, Ricard and Berger are all brand names of a certain kind of spirit. What is it?

10

QUIZ 46

 Where does the word 'tiddly', meaning 'slightly drunk' come from?

8

 Which painter was addicted to both absinthe and turpentine?

2

 Whose last movie was 'The Misfits' in 1961, before she died of an alcohol and barbiturate overdose?

10

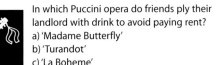 In which Puccini opera do friends ply their landlord with drink to avoid paying rent?
a) 'Madame Butterfly'
b) 'Turandot'
c) 'La Boheme'

4

 In Australian drinking slang, what is a 'butcher'?
a) A very small glass of beer
b) Someone with a voracious appetite for alcohol
c) A cocktail of all the spirits on the bar

6

How many gallons of beer are consumed
in Germany each year, during the Oktoberfest?
a) 2.6 million
b) 1.2 million
c) 5.5 million

QUIZ 47

Why did the English Navy refer to rum as 'Nelson's blood'?
a) Sailors took their lime juice ration with it
b) Nelson's body was shipped home in a cask of rum, which was then returned to service
c) Lady Emma Hamilton's favorite tipple was rum

8

Which Stephen King novel features a woman whose drunken husband 'accidentally' falls to his death in a disused well?

4

BONUS

Which movie features Eddie Murphy and Martin Lawrence on a bootlegging run to Mississippi during Prohibition?

10

Which British 1980s song duo was described as 'Tommy Cooper backed by a bad Shirley Bassey', before the lead singer descended into drugs and alcohol?

6

What is 'ebriosity'?

2

QUIZ 48

Where does the word 'boozer' come from?
a) The East End of London
b) Egypt
c) India

6

Which fictional character keeps an obsessive diary of her calorie, alcohol and cigarette intake?

4

Which Celtic actor and reformed alcoholic said, "I wanted to go to sleep rather than pass out, and I wanted to wake up rather than come to"?

8

Which Irish band wrote 'Whiskey in the Jar'?
a) Thin Lizzy
b) Boomtown Rats
c) U2

2

Which well-known drink has an original gravity of 1,000?

10

QUIZ 49

In the 1950s, the Chateauneuf Du Pape wine estate forbade what sort of trespass?
a) Trespass by dogs
b) Trespass by light aircraft
c) Trespass by UFOs

10

Where, according to the New Testament, did Christ turn water into wine?

4

Which US comedy star was found dead of an overdose at the 'Chateau Marmont' hotel in Hollywood on 5 March 1982?

2

Name the Verdi opera, that includes a prolonged toast to the beauty of its heroine.
a) 'Aida'
b) 'Rigoletto'
c) 'La Traviata'

6

Why should champagne glasses always be completely dry?

8

QUIZ 50

In which year did Prohibition begin in the US?
a) 1919
b) 1921
c) 1922

4

Who wrote, "…the awful pubs where people talked and a lot of the talk was rubbish…".
a) Lord Beaverbrook
b) Keith Waterhouse
c) Robert Maxwell

8

Which actor decided to sober up after being found 'running naked through the jungles of Mexico'?

2

Tracy Chapman wrote the lyrics 'speed so fast felt like I was drunk', to which song?

10

What cocktail is named after the Californian surfer Tom Harvey, because of his behavior when drunk?

6

SOLUTIONS

QUIZ 1 – SOLUTIONS

 b) Ruth Ellis

 c) The Book of Isaiah in the Old Testament

 b) Lie on the floor without holding on

 'Wonderful Tonight'

 No guns

QUIZ 2 – SOLUTIONS

 c) 1775

 F Scott Fitzgerald

 Bryan Brown

 Jim Morrison of 'The Doors'

 b) It falls over onto its right side

QUIZ 3 – SOLUTIONS

 True

 He spontaneously combusted!

 b) 'The Quiet Man'

 'The Who'

 c) As drunk as Chloe

QUIZ 4 – SOLUTIONS

 c) Cirrhosis of the liver

 b) The Second Earl of Rochester, John Wilmot

 Dennis Hopper

 Tom Waits

 False

QUIZ 5 – SOLUTIONS

 False – he is the Greek god of fertility and wine

 c) 'A Tale of Two Cities' by Charles Dickens

 Whoopi Goldberg

 Gin

 a) A Caribbean rumrunner

 c) El Lager

QUIZ 6 – SOLUTIONS

 b) German submarines

 Dorothy L Sayers

 'The Slaughtered Lamb'

 Ludvig Van Beethoven

 a) …makes me feel good"

QUIZ 7 – SOLUTIONS

 He was put in the stocks

 True

 A vodka martini

 c) Music by Mozart was played to assist fermentation

 a) A drink before breakfast

QUIZ 8 – SOLUTIONS

 If someone was sick over the side of prison ships, they'd shout "Watch under!", which became 'chunder'

 a) Someone you don't like who drinks as much as you

 Harvey

 a) Dean Martin

 Australia

 c) The ring-pull

QUIZ 9 – SOLUTIONS

 c) Egyptians

 'The Iceman Cometh'

 The Pan Galactic Gargle Blaster

 Chicago

 a) An Oxford University beer challenge

QUIZ 10 – SOLUTIONS

 b) His recently severed arm

 Absinthe

 True

 Neil Diamond

 b) A free ration of beer for brewers

QUIZ 11 – SOLUTIONS

 a) Drinking too much 'small beer' on a hot day

 False – the figure was four million!

 False – Burt Lancaster did

 Frank Sinatra, Dean Martin, Sammy Davis Jr

 b) Water

 a) A cocktail of beer and gin

QUIZ 12 – SOLUTIONS

 c) To protect themselves from the drink's noxious fumes

 Because another author told him that 'serious writers' didn't drink them

 Bluto

 Charlie Parker – the film of his life was called 'Bird'

 c) An enormous two-handled drinking mug

QUIZ 13 – SOLUTIONS

 True – beer was cleaner and safer than water

 Charles Bukowski

 a) Meg Ryan

 b) Milk

 Irish spirit made from potato

QUIZ 14 – SOLUTIONS

 a) Cabbage

 c) …the host"

 c) …pass the beer nuts"

 True

 False

 a) They overturn in six to eight minutes

QUIZ 15 – SOLUTIONS

 a) 1935

 George Bernard Shaw

 He believes that the fluoridation of tap water is a communist mind plot

 False

 c) The Liffey

QUIZ 16 – SOLUTIONS

 b) Reno, Nevada

 b) "That drunken fool"

 'Animal House'

 'Wild Thing'

 c) The US Air Force

QUIZ 17 – SOLUTIONS

 True

 Branwell Brontë

 'The Lost Weekend'

 a) Marc Bolan – he was killed in a car crash

 b) A type of white grape

 a) "Oh, come quickly. I am drinking the stars"

QUIZ 18 – SOLUTIONS

 True

 b) Ernest Hemingway

 Grape Knee-Hi

 A Prairie Oyster – raw egg with Worcester sauce

 a) …speak'

QUIZ 19 – SOLUTIONS

 a) Winston Churchill's mother

 a) Pablo Picasso

 Errol Flynn

 Peter Ilyich Tchaikovsky

 Cider

QUIZ 20 – SOLUTIONS

 The town of Pilsn in the Czech Republic

 a) Wendy Wasserstein

 b) Christian Slater

 Bessie Smith

 Very Special Old Pale

 b) Drinking chocolate mixed with milk, wine, or beer

QUIZ 21 – SOLUTIONS

 False – her name was Ninkasi

 Noah

 'Duff'

 b) 'I am a Cider Drinker'

 b) Drink alone

QUIZ 22 – SOLUTIONS

 c) Pouring a pint on a chair and then sitting in it wearing leather trousers

 a) Christopher Sly

 Rob Lowe

 Hank Williams

 Switzerland

QUIZ 23 – SOLUTIONS

 True

 a) Francois Rabelais

 b) Shitsurakuen

 Billy Joel

 c) Fish's air bladders

 c) 97 per cent

QUIZ 24 – SOLUTIONS

 b) 1879

 a) A butt of malmsey

 Boston

 Nero

 The 'Oktoberfest' in Germany

QUIZ 25 – SOLUTIONS

 True

 Christopher Marlowe

 b) Shirley Maclaine

 'Led Zeppelin'

 b) A German vineyard

QUIZ 26 – SOLUTIONS

 c) He poured molten lead down their throats

 a) Socrates

 'The Viper Room'

 'Copacabana'

 WC Fields

 c) New York

QUIZ 27 – SOLUTIONS

 Women were banned from getting drunk

 'Alice in Wonderland' by Lewis Carroll

 a) Moe Syzlac

 Emmylou Harris

 b) George

QUIZ 28 – SOLUTIONS

 True

 c) Falstaff

 John Huston

 True

 b) New Zealand

QUIZ 29 – SOLUTIONS

 True

 Pablo Picasso

 a) Greta Garbo

 Garth Brooks

 a) Italy

 a) Queensland

QUIZ 30 – SOLUTIONS

 a) A lidless barrel with a head hole

 Tennessee Williams

 Oliver Reed

 a) 'Bucks Fizz'

 12 – a firkin is nine gallons, and a butt is 108 gallons

QUIZ 31 – SOLUTIONS

 a) A ship's water barrel

 Arthur Rimbaud

 c) Vonda Shepherd

 'The Who'

 Abraham Lincoln

QUIZ 32 – SOLUTIONS

 a) Elizabeth I

 Laurie Lee

 Drew Barrymore

 George Jones

 c) A person who cannot control their drinking

 a) Randy Hanzlick

QUIZ 33 – SOLUTIONS

 c) Nose paint

 Anna Wintour

 Hannibal Lecter, in the classic thriller 'Silence of the Lambs'

 Eric Clapton

 c) Frequently indulging in alcohol

QUIZ 34 – SOLUTIONS

 b) Alaska

 TS Eliot

 Richard Harris

 'The Barber of Seville'

 c) Chateau Cilla

QUIZ 35 – SOLUTIONS

 c) 11,000,000 gallons

 He accidentally shot himself while cleaning his gun

 Orson Welles

 Judy Garland, who appeared with Liza Minnelli

 b) Sweat

 a) Fear of drinks

QUIZ 36 – SOLUTIONS

 a) A pus-colored liqueur

 Lemon Coke

 Robert Shaw

 Dean Martin

 b) The distance between the wine and the cork in a bottle

QUIZ 37 – SOLUTIONS

 b) 1759

 'Juno and the Paycock'

 c) George Best

 'Definitely Maybe'

 a) A labologist

QUIZ 38 – SOLUTIONS

 False – it was actually a seventeenth-century tawny wine

 Edouard Manet

 a) A five-dollar milkshake

 Robbie Williams

 b) Gin

 a) 1850

85

QUIZ 39 – SOLUTIONS

 c) Queen Victoria

 'The Tenant of Wildfell Hall'

 Paul Hogan

 Ron McKernan

 c) 8 per cent

QUIZ 40 – SOLUTIONS

 a) the lord's professional ale tester

 Peter O'Toole

 Elizabeth Taylor and Richard Burton

 'Duran Duran'

 Wormwood

QUIZ 41 – SOLUTIONS

 a) 1933

 James Joyce

 'True Grit'

 Janis Joplin

 b) Its color (it means 'light')

 c) Placing a live eel in the drinker's full cup

QUIZ 42 – SOLUTIONS

 True – he was overcome by the alcohol

 Henri de Toulouse Lautrec

 a) Michael Caine

 Diana Ross

 b) Japan

QUIZ 43 – SOLUTIONS

 True

 a) 'L'Assomoir'

 b) Roscoe (Fatty) Arbuckle

 Leonard Cohen, aka 'The Godfather of Gloom' or 'Laughing Lennie'

 Any strange and unpleasant mixture of drinks, eg milk and beer

QUIZ 44 – SOLUTIONS

 b) Fufluns

 Laudanum

 Leonard Rossiter and Joan Collins

 a) Little Richard

 Measuring alcohol content

 c) St Amand of Maastricht

QUIZ 45 – SOLUTIONS

 a) 3 per cent

 Al Pacino

 b) Jessica Lange

 Elkie Brookes

 Pastis

QUIZ 46 – SOLUTIONS

 Tiddly Wink, which rhymes with drink

 Vincent Van Gogh – he used the turpentine to thin his paint and developed a taste for it

 Marilyn Monroe

 c) 'La Boheme'

 a) A very small glass of beer

QUIZ 47 – SOLUTIONS

 b) Nelson's body was shipped home in a cask of rum which was then returned to service

 'Dolores Claiborne'

 'Life'

 'Soft Cell'

 Habitual drunkenness

 b) 1.2 million

QUIZ 48 – SOLUTIONS

 b) Egypt

 Bridget Jones, in the book of the same name by Helen Fielding

 Anthony Hopkins

 a) Thin Lizzy

 Water

QUIZ 49 – SOLUTIONS

 c) Trespass by UFOs

 At the marriage feast of Canaan

 John Belushi

 c) 'La Traviata'

 Any wetness kills the bubbles

QUIZ 50 – SOLUTIONS

 a) 1919

 b) Keith Waterhouse

 Dennis Hopper

 'Fast Car'

 Harvey Wallbanger